AS Physics

There's a big jump from GCSE to AS Physics.
And with modules to take as early as January, you need to
make sure you hit the ground running.

This book will give you a Head Start — it covers all those things that
trip you up when you move from GCSE to AS, and includes loads of
practice questions to make sure you've got the hang of it all.

Spend the first week of 6th form or (whisper it quietly) the summer holiday working
through it so everything will make perfect sense when you start your AS.

We've done our bit — the rest is up to you.

What CGP is all about

Our sole aim here at CGP is to produce the highest quality books
— carefully written, immaculately presented and dangerously
close to being funny.

Then we work our socks off to get them out to you
— at the cheapest possible prices.

Published by CGP

Author:
Richard Tattersall

Editors:
Amy Boutal, Julie Wakeling, Sarah Williams

With thanks to Glenn Rogers for the proofreading

ISBN: 978 1 84762 115 3

Groovy website: www.cgpbooks.co.uk
Jolly bits of clipart from CorelDRAW®
Printed by Elanders Ltd, Newcastle upon Tyne.

Based on the classic CGP style created by Richard Parsons.

Contents

Symbols and SI Units

One of the biggest jumps between GCSE Physics and AS Physics is in the way things are written down. At AS level, you're expected to start using <u>standard scientific notation</u>...

Standard notation means:

- using the <u>conventional</u> symbols for quantities,
  e.g. a temperature should always have the symbol T
- writing all quantities in terms of SI units (<u>Système International</u>)
- writing very large and very small numbers in standard form (e.g. 10^6 or 10^{-3})

That last point means you shouldn't have to worry about meeting nasty units like microseconds (μs) and megajoules (MJ) in exams. They'll usually be written as 10^{-6} s and 10^6 J instead. (If you can't remember how standard index form works, look it up in one of our maths guides... or phone a friend.)

You still need to learn the unit prefixes though, because textbooks use them — see below.

The table below lists the different quantities you'll meet in this book, with their standard symbols and units.

Quantity	Symbol	Unit Name	Unit Symbol
Displacement (distance)	s	metre	m
Time	t	second	s
Velocity (speed)	v	metre per second	$m\,s^{-1}$
Acceleration	a	metre per second squared	$m\,s^{-2}$
Mass	m	kilogram	kg
Force	F	newton	N
Gravitational field strength	g	newton per kilogram	$N\,kg^{-1}$
Energy	E	joule	J
Power	P	watt	W
Frequency	f	hertz	Hz
Wavelength	λ	metre	m
Temperature	T	kelvin	K
Charge	Q	coulomb	C
Electric current	I	amp	A
Potential difference	V	volt	V
Resistance	R	ohm	Ω

At A Level, units like m/s are written $m\,s^{-1}$. This is just <u>index notation</u>. (If it doesn't make sense to you, look up 'rules of indices' in a maths book.)

If you write the unit out in full, it should be all lower case — always.

If the unit comes from someone's name, the symbol should start with a capital letter e.g. Hz.

Here are the unit prefixes for those long numbers:

Multiple	Prefix	Symbol
10^{12}	tera	T
10^9	giga	G
10^6	mega	M
10^3	kilo	k
10^{-2}	centi	c
10^{-3}	milli	m
10^{-6}	micro	μ
10^{-9}	nano	n
10^{-12}	pico	p
10^{-15}	femto	f

Of course, what they don't tell you at AS is that people in the real world don't use standard scientific notation. A lot of textbooks that you'll be using will stick to the old prefix system for units.

And you'll also meet odd units like parsecs, electonvolts and atomic mass units, which are definitely not SI.

Distance, Time and Speed

Distance, Time and Speed

Points A and B are separated by a distance in metres. Now imagine a spider walking from A to B — you can measure the time it takes, in seconds, for it to travel this distance.

Well aren't you a cutie...

You can then work out the average speed of the spider between the two points using the equation (which I'm sure you all know by now):

speed (ms⁻¹) = distance travelled (m) / time taken (s)

This is a very useful equation, but it does have a couple of <u>limitations</u>:

1) It only tells you the <u>average</u> speed. The spider could have varied its speed from fast to slow and even gone backwards. So long as it got from A to B in the same time you get the same answer.

2) We assume that the spider takes the <u>shortest possible path</u> between the two points (a straight line), rather than meandering around.

It's important to remember that you should always convert distances to metres, times to seconds and speeds to metres per second...

E.g. A time of 12 minutes is 12 x 60 s = 720 s.
A distance of 30 km is 30 x 1000 m = 30 000 m.
A speed of 10 km per minute is (10 x 1000) / 60 ms⁻¹ = 167 ms⁻¹.

Now have a go at these questions:

1) A cricket ball is thrown 40 m at a speed of 18 ms⁻¹. How long does it take?

2) A sprinter runs the 100 m in a time of 10.5 s. What is his average speed?

3) A walker travels at an average speed of 0.5 ms⁻¹ for half an hour. How far do they walk?

4) A cyclist travels 10 km at an average speed of 8 ms⁻¹. How long does it take her?

5) A ferry crosses a 250 m wide river in 2 minutes. What is its average speed?

6) The speed of light is 3×10^8 ms⁻¹. If it takes light from the Sun about 8 minutes to reach us, what is the approximate distance from the Earth to the Sun?

7) A parrot flies 15 m between trees in 5 s. What is its average speed?

8) How long will it take a horse to gallop 300 m across a field at an average speed of 15 ms⁻¹?

9) A spaceship flies 3000 km in 1 minute. What is its average speed?

10) A blade of grass grows at an average speed of 1 metre per year. How far does it grow in one week?

Displacement

Displacement — a Vector Quantity

To get from point A to point B you need to know what direction to travel in — just knowing the distance you need to travel isn't enough. This information, distance plus direction, is known as the _displacement_ from A to B and has the symbol s. It's a _vector_ quantity since all vectors have both a size and a direction.

Representing Displacement — Scale Drawings

The simplest way to draw a displacement is to draw an arrow — the length of the arrow tells you the distance, and the way the arrow points shows you the direction.

A   B

You can do this even for very large displacements so long as you scale down.

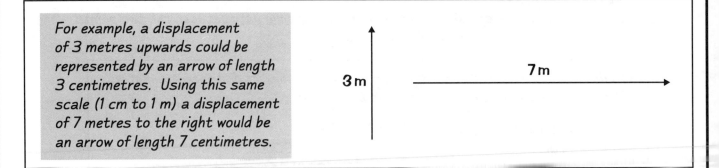

For example, a displacement of 3 metres upwards could be represented by an arrow of length 3 centimetres. Using this same scale (1 cm to 1 m) a displacement of 7 metres to the right would be an arrow of length 7 centimetres.

3 m

7 m

Addition of Two Displacements

To add two displacements, you can't simply add together the two distances as this doesn't account for the different directions of the displacements. What you do is:

1)   Draw arrows representing the two vectors.
2)   Place the arrows one after the other "tip-to-tail".
3)   Draw a third arrow from start to finish. This is your total displacement.

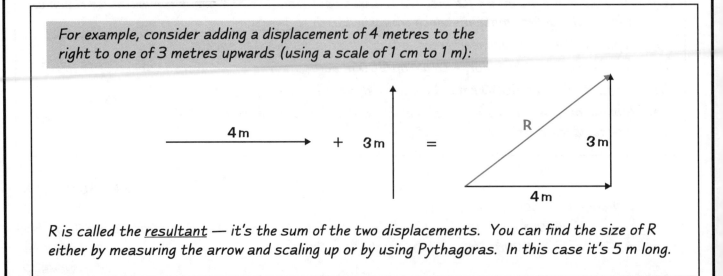

For example, consider adding a displacement of 4 metres to the right to one of 3 metres upwards (using a scale of 1 cm to 1 m):

4 m   +   3 m   =   R   3 m   4 m

R is called the _resultant_ — it's the sum of the two displacements. You can find the size of R either by measuring the arrow and scaling up or by using Pythagoras. In this case it's 5 m long.

Displacement

Have a go at these questions:

1) Draw arrows representing the following displacements to the given scale.
   - (a) 3 miles upwards (1 cm to 1 mile)
   - (b) 12 m to the right (1 cm to 2 m)
   - (c) 4 mm downwards (1 cm to 1 mm)
   - (d) 3.5 km north-east (1 cm to 1 km)
   - (e) 5 cm south-west (1 cm to 1 cm)
   - (f) 24 m at a bearing of 030° (1 cm to 5 m)
   - (g) 110 miles at a bearing of 210° (1 cm to 20 miles)
   - (h) 9 mm at a bearing of 330° (1 cm to 2 mm)
   - (i) 18 km north-west (1 cm to 5 km)
   - (j) 9 miles to the left (1 cm to 2 miles)

2) Find the lengths of the following displacements by drawing the arrows "tip-to-tail".
   - (a) 5 m right and 12 m up
   - (b) 8 m up and 4 m left
   - (c) 6 cm right and 8 cm left
   - (d) 15 miles down and 20 miles left
   - (e) 3 mm left and 12 mm right
   - (f) 7.5 cm up and 9.5 cm right
   - (g) 7 km down and 24 km right
   - (h) 20 m left and 30 m down
   - (i) 40 miles left and 50 miles right
   - (j) 60 mm up and 20 mm right

Answers

2) (a) 13 m   (d) 25 miles   (g) 25 km   (i) 63.2 mm

(b) 8.94 m   (e) 9 mm   (h) 36.1 m   (j) 10 miles

(c) 2 cm   (f) 12.1 cm

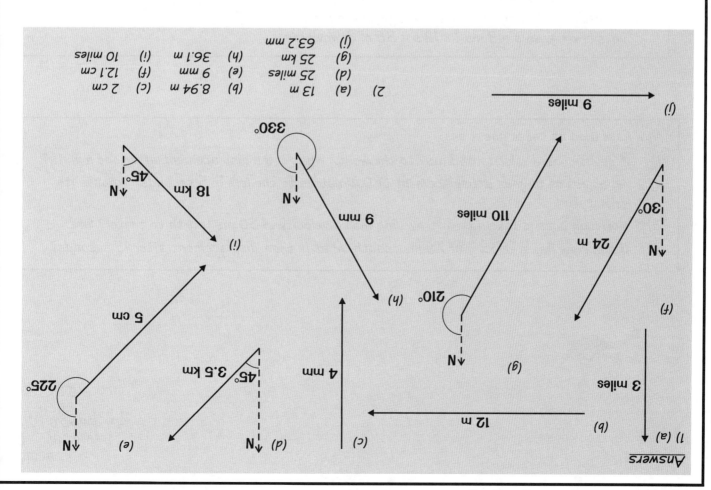

Velocity

Another quantity that you'll have to get used to using is _velocity_, symbol v.

The Relationship Between Displacement and Velocity

The velocity of an object is given by the following equation:

velocity (ms^{-1}) = displacement (m) / time taken (t)

Or, in symbols:

$$v = s / t$$

This equation is very similar to the one relating speed and distance (page 1), except that it includes information about the direction of motion.

Examples:

1) An object is displaced 100 metres to the right in a time of 4 seconds.
   What is its velocity?

   v = s/t, so v = 100 m / 4 s = 25 ms^{-1} to the right.
   Velocity's a vector (see next page), so you have to quote the direction as well as the speed.

2) A seed has a velocity of 3 metres per second downwards.
   What is its displacement after 12 seconds?

   v = s/t. Multiplying both sides by t gives v × t = s,
   i.e. s = v × t, so s = 3 ms^{-1} × 12 s = 36 m downwards.

Now have a go at these questions:

1) A giraffe has a velocity of 3 ms^{-1} to the west. What is its displacement after one minute?
2) An object undergoes a displacement of 0.2 metres to the left in 5 seconds. What is its velocity?
3) How long does it take a train travelling with a velocity of 50 ms^{-1} north to travel 1 km?
4) If someone has a velocity of 7.5 ms^{-1} south, what is their displacement after 15 seconds?

Answers
1) 180 m west
2) 0.04 ms^{-1} left
3) 20 s
4) 112.5 m south

Velocity

Velocity is Another Vector Quantity

Just as displacement is distance and direction, velocity is the <u>speed</u> and direction of an object.

Again, you can represent velocities with arrows, but now the longer the arrow, the greater the speed of the object. A typical scale might be 1 cm to 1 ms^{-1}.

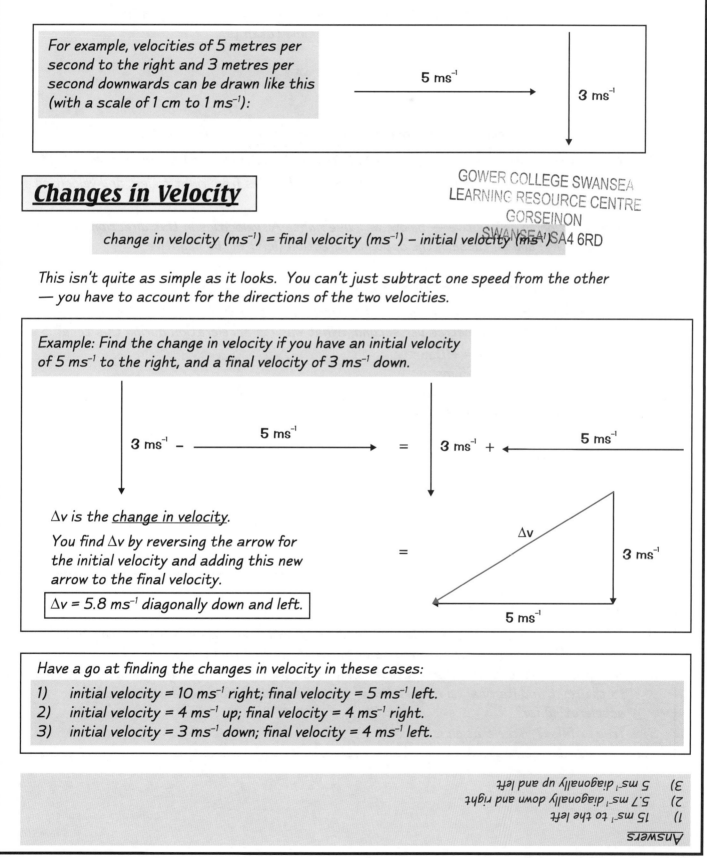

For example, velocities of 5 metres per second to the right and 3 metres per second downwards can be drawn like this (with a scale of 1 cm to 1 ms^{-1}):

5 ms^{-1}

3 ms^{-1}

Changes in Velocity

change in velocity (ms^{-1}) = final velocity (ms^{-1}) – initial velocity (ms^{-1})

This isn't quite as simple as it looks. You can't just subtract one speed from the other — you have to account for the directions of the two velocities.

Example: Find the change in velocity if you have an initial velocity of 5 ms^{-1} to the right, and a final velocity of 3 ms^{-1} down.

3 ms^{-1} – 5 ms^{-1} = 3 ms^{-1} + 5 ms^{-1}

Δv is the <u>change in velocity</u>.

You find Δv by reversing the arrow for the initial velocity and adding this new arrow to the final velocity.

$\Delta v = 5.8$ ms^{-1} diagonally down and left.

= Δv 3 ms^{-1} 5 ms^{-1}

Have a go at finding the changes in velocity in these cases:

1) initial velocity = 10 ms^{-1} right; final velocity = 5 ms^{-1} left.
2) initial velocity = 4 ms^{-1} up; final velocity = 4 ms^{-1} right.
3) initial velocity = 3 ms^{-1} down; final velocity = 4 ms^{-1} left.

Answers
1) 15 ms^{-1} to the left
2) 5.7 ms^{-1} diagonally down and right
3) 5 ms^{-1} diagonally up and left

6

Acceleration

Acceleration — the Change in Velocity Every Second

Acceleration (in metres per second^2) = $\dfrac{\text{change in velocity of an object (in metres per second)}}{\text{time taken (seconds)}}$

So,

Acceleration (ms^{-2}) = $\dfrac{\text{final velocity (ms}^{-1}) - \text{initial velocity (ms}^{-1})}{\text{time taken (s)}}$

Or in symbols:

$$a = \frac{v - u}{t} = \frac{\Delta v}{t}$$

It's often useful to only think about velocities in <u>one dimension</u>, say left to right.

This has the advantage that you don't need to bother drawing out all the arrows for the velocities.

But you still need to recognise the difference between velocities from right to left and velocities from left to right.

Choose a direction to be positive — below, we'll use right. All velocities in this direction will from now on be positive, and all those in the opposite direction (left) will be negative.

Look at these examples to see how this works:

1) A car starts off moving to the right at 10 metres per second. After 20 seconds it is moving to the left at 5 metres per second. What was its acceleration during this time?
$u = 10$ ms^{-1} to the right = +10 ms^{-1}
$v = 5$ ms^{-1} to the left = −5 ms^{-1}
So, $a = (v - u)/t = (-5$ ms$^{-1} - 10$ ms$^{-1}) / 20$ s $= (-15$ ms$^{-1}) / 20$ s $= -0.75$ ms^{-2}.
The acceleration is negative so it's to the left.

2) An object accelerates from rest at 5 ms^{-2} to the right. If its final velocity is 20 ms^{-1} to the right, how long does it accelerate for?
$u = 0$
$v = 20$ ms^{-1} to the right = +20 ms^{-1}
$a = (v - u)/t$, multiplying both sides by t gives $t \times a = v - u$, dividing both sides by a gives $t = (v - u)/a$.
So, $t = (20$ ms$^{-1} - 0) / (5$ ms$^{-2}) = 4$ s.

Have a go at these questions:

1) A train has an initial velocity of 12 ms^{-1} to the left. After 20 seconds it is moving to the right at 18 ms^{-1}. What was its average acceleration during this time?
2) A ship accelerates at a uniform rate of 0.1 ms^{-2} to the right. If its initial velocity is 1.5 ms^{-1} to the right and its final velocity is 4 ms^{-1} in the same direction, how long has it been accelerating for?
3) True or false? Acceleration is a vector.

6
Answers
1) 1.5 ms^{-2} to the right
2) 25 s
3) True

Acceleration

Falling — the Acceleration Due to Gravity

When an object is dropped, it accelerates downwards at a constant rate of roughly 9.8 ms^{-2}. This is the <u>acceleration due to gravity</u>.

It seems sensible to take the upward direction as positive and down as negative, making the acceleration due to gravity <u>-9.8 ms^{-2}</u>.

Look at the following examples (ignore air resistance and horizontal motion):

1) What is the vertical velocity of a skydiver 5 seconds after jumping out of a plane?

$u = 0$
$a = -9.8 \text{ ms}^{-2}$
Example 2 on page 6 gives $t \times a = v - u$,
so adding u to each side gives $v = u + (t \times a)$.
So $v = 0 + (5 \text{ s} \times -9.8 \text{ ms}^{-2}) = 0 - 49 \text{ ms}^{-1}$
$= -49 \text{ ms}^{-1} = 49 \text{ ms}^{-1}$ down.

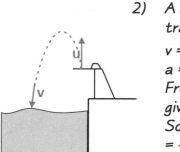

2) A diver jumps up off a springboard. After 2 seconds he hits the water travelling downwards at 18 ms^{-1}. What was his initial vertical velocity?

$v = 18 \text{ ms}^{-1}$ down $= -18 \text{ ms}^{-1}$
$a = -9.8 \text{ ms}^{-2}$
From example 1, $v = u + (t \times a)$. Subtracting $(t \times a)$ from each side gives $v - (t \times a) = u$.
So, $u = -18 \text{ ms}^{-1} - (2 \text{ s} \times -9.8 \text{ ms}^{-2}) = -18 \text{ ms}^{-1} - (-19.6 \text{ ms}^{-1})$
$= -18 \text{ ms}^{-1} + 19.6 \text{ ms}^{-1} = 1.6 \text{ ms}^{-1} = 1.6 \text{ ms}^{-1}$ upwards.

Try these — in each case you can ignore air resistance.
(Hint: it's often useful to draw a little diagram of what's going on in these questions.)

1) An apple falls from a tree and hits the ground at 4.9 ms^{-1}. For how long was it falling?

2) A penny dropped from the top of a tall building falls for 3 seconds. With what velocity does it hit the ground?

3) A stone is thrown downwards. It hits the ground at 26 ms^{-1} after 2 seconds. With what velocity was it thrown?

4) A metal rod falls from a stationary helicopter. With what velocity does it hit the ground 10 seconds later?

5) A sandbag is dropped from a stationary hot-air balloon and it hits the ground at a velocity of 24.5 metres per second downwards. How long was it falling for?

6) A ball is thrown upwards. After 2 seconds it is caught moving downwards at 10 ms^{-1}. With what velocity was it thrown?

Displacement-Time Graphs

Drawing Graphs to Show How Far Something Has Travelled

A graph of displacement against time tells you <u>how far</u> an object is from a given point, in a given direction, as time goes on. As the object moves away from that point the displacement on the graph goes up, and as it moves towards it the displacement goes down:

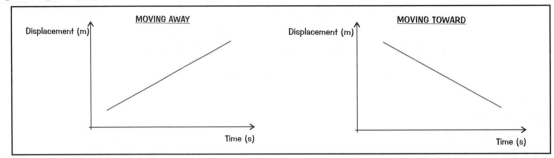

Importantly, these graphs only tell you about motion in <u>one dimension</u> — for example, they can tell you how far up a ball has been thrown, but not how far it has moved horizontally.
You can use these graphs to calculate the velocity of an object (in the given direction).

This example shows the displacement-time graph for a cyclist accelerating to a constant speed and then braking.

You can read the following <u>directly</u> off the graph:

1) He took 20 seconds to accelerate to full speed.
2) He travelled 100 metres in that time.
3) He travelled at constant velocity for the next 10 seconds.
4) He travelled 200 metres in that time.
5) He took 5 seconds to stop fully.
6) He travelled 50 metres in that time.
7) He remained stationary at a displacement of 350 metres from his starting point.

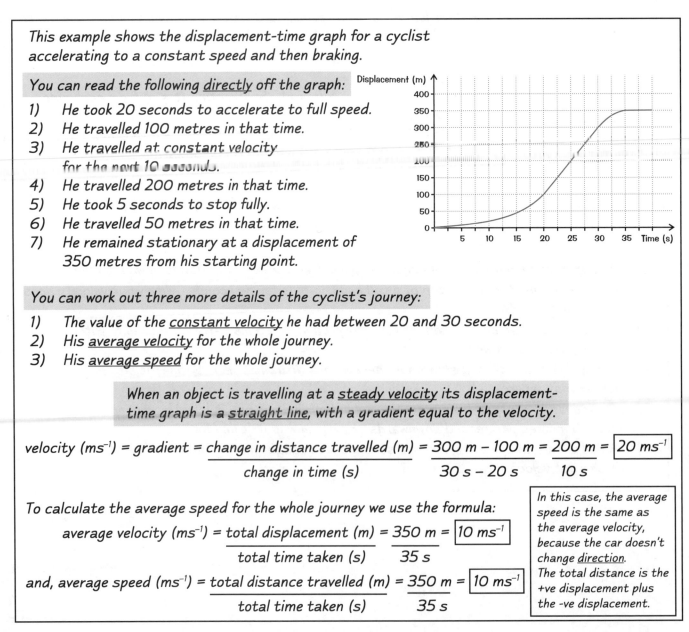

You can work out three more details of the cyclist's journey:

1) The value of the <u>constant velocity</u> he had between 20 and 30 seconds.
2) His <u>average velocity</u> for the whole journey.
3) His <u>average speed</u> for the whole journey.

> When an object is travelling at a <u>steady velocity</u> its displacement-time graph is a <u>straight line</u>, with a gradient equal to the velocity.

velocity (ms⁻¹) = gradient = $\dfrac{\text{change in distance travelled (m)}}{\text{change in time (s)}}$ = $\dfrac{300\,m - 100\,m}{30\,s - 20\,s}$ = $\dfrac{200\,m}{10\,s}$ = $\boxed{20\ ms^{-1}}$

To calculate the average speed for the whole journey we use the formula:

average velocity (ms⁻¹) = $\dfrac{\text{total displacement (m)}}{\text{total time taken (s)}}$ = $\dfrac{350\,m}{35\,s}$ = $\boxed{10\ ms^{-1}}$

and, average speed (ms⁻¹) = $\dfrac{\text{total distance travelled (m)}}{\text{total time taken (s)}}$ = $\dfrac{350\,m}{35\,s}$ = $\boxed{10\ ms^{-1}}$

*In this case, the average speed is the same as the average velocity, because the car doesn't change <u>direction</u>.
The total distance is the +ve displacement plus the -ve displacement.*

Displacement-Time Graphs

Have a go at analysing these graphs:

Write down as much as you can about the motion of the objects represented by the following graphs. Work out any steady velocities, the average velocity and average speed for each journey.

Graph 1:

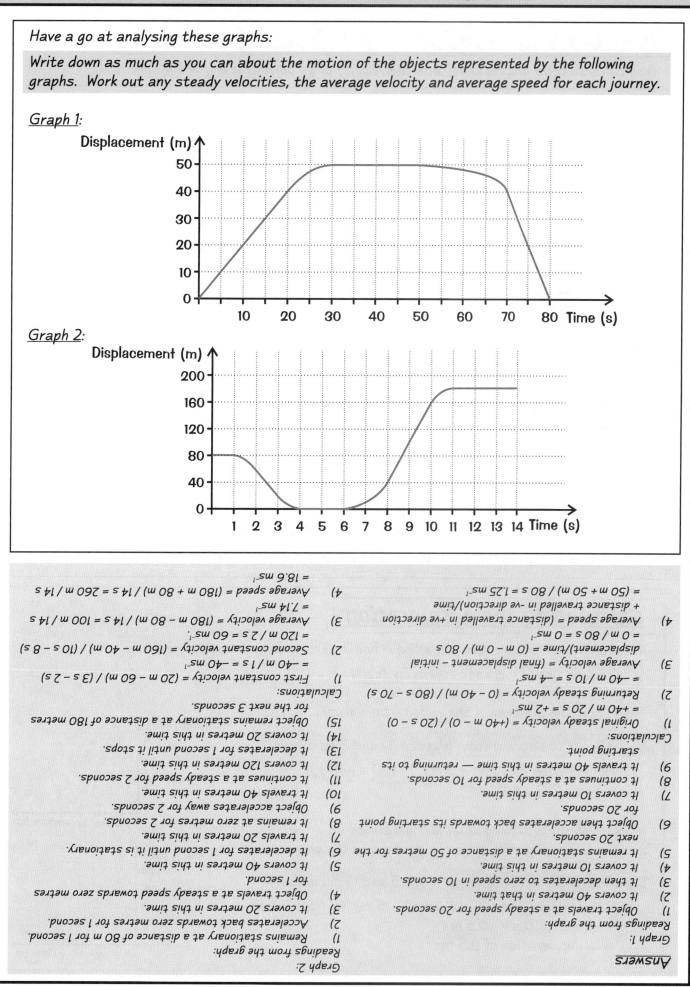

Graph 1:

Readings from the graph:
1) Object travels at a steady speed for 20 seconds.
2) It covers 40 metres in that time.
3) It then decelerates to zero speed in 10 seconds.
4) It covers 10 metres in this time.
5) It remains stationary at a distance of 50 metres for the next 20 seconds.
6) Object then accelerates back towards its starting point for 20 seconds.
7) It covers 10 metres in this time.
8) It continues at a steady speed for 10 seconds.
9) It travels 40 metres in this time — returning to its starting point.

Calculations:
1) Original steady velocity = (+40 m – 0) / (20 s – 0)
   = +40 m / 20 s = +2 ms⁻¹
2) Returning steady velocity = (0 – 40 m) / (80 s – 70 s)
   = –40 m / 10 s = – 4 ms⁻¹
3) Average velocity = (final displacement – initial displacement)/time
   = (0 m – 0 m) / 80 s
   = 0 m / 80 s = 0 ms⁻¹
4) Average speed = (distance travelled in +ve direction + distance travelled in –ve direction)/time
   = (50 m + 50 m) / 80 s = 1.25 ms⁻¹

Graph 2:

Readings from the graph:
1) Remains stationary at a distance of 80 m for 1 second.
2) Accelerates back towards zero metres for 1 second.
3) It covers 20 metres in this time.
4) Object travels at a steady speed towards zero metres for 1 second.
5) It covers 40 metres in this time.
6) It decelerates for 1 second until it is stationary.
7) It travels 20 metres in this time.
8) It remains at zero metres for 2 seconds.
9) Object accelerates away for 2 seconds.
10) It travels 40 metres in this time.
11) It continues at a steady speed for 2 seconds.
12) It covers 120 metres in this time.
13) It decelerates for 1 second until it stops.
14) It covers 20 metres in this time.
15) Object remains stationary at a distance of 180 metres for the next 3 seconds.

Calculations:
1) First constant velocity = (20 m – 60 m) / (3 s – 2 s)
   = –40 m / 1 s = –40 ms⁻¹
2) Second constant velocity = (160 m – 40 m) / (10 s – 8 s)
   = 120 m / 2 s = 60 ms⁻¹
3) Average velocity = (180 m – 80 m) / 14 s = 100 m / 14 s
   = 7.14 ms⁻¹
4) Average speed = (180 m + 80 m) / 14 s = 260 m / 14 s
   = 18.6 ms⁻¹

Velocity-Time Graphs

Drawing Graphs to Show the Velocity of an Object

You can also draw graphs that show the velocity of an object moving in one dimension.

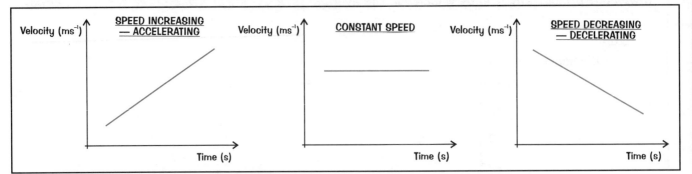

You can use a velocity-time graph to calculate two things:
1) The distance the object has moved.
2) The acceleration.

Calculating the Distance Travelled

To find the distance an object travels between two times:
1) Draw vertical lines up from the horizontal axis at the two times, as shown.
2) Work out the area of the shape formed by these lines.
3) When you work out the area, you're multiplying time (the horizontal length) by average speed (the average vertical length), so the result is a distance.

E.g. What is the distance travelled between 2 seconds and 4 seconds?

The shape is a trapezium, so the area = ½(a + b) × h = ½(4 + 6) × 2 = 5 ms^{-1} × 2 s = 10 m.

Calculating the Acceleration

The acceleration of an object travelling in one dimension is given (see page 6) by:

Acceleration (ms^{-2}) = $\dfrac{\text{change in velocity } (ms^{-1})}{\text{time taken } (s)}$

This is just the gradient of the velocity-time graph.

E.g. What is the acceleration between 10 and 20 seconds?

Acceleration = (4 ms^{-1} – 3 ms^{-1}) / (20 s – 10 s)
= 1 ms^{-1} / 10 s = 0.1 ms^{-2}

When an object is slowing down (decelerating), its acceleration is negative, as is the gradient of the graph.

E.g. What is the acceleration between 5 and 15 seconds?

Acceleration (in ms^{-2}) = (10 ms^{-1} – 15 ms^{-1}) / (15 s – 5 s)
= –5 ms^{-1} / 10 s = –0.5 ms^{-2}
or a deceleration of 0.5 ms^{-2}

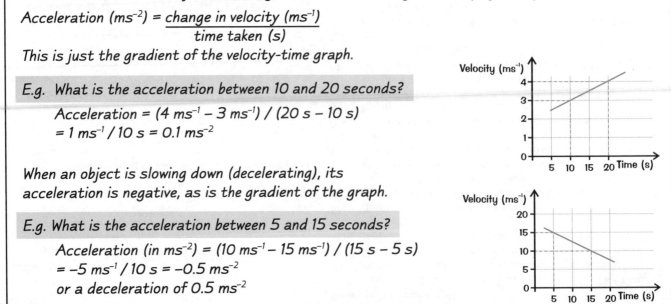

Velocity-Time Graphs

Try these:

1) Calculate the accelerations in each of the three sections of each graph.
2) Calculate the distances travelled in each of the three sections of each graph and calculate the total distance travelled in each case.

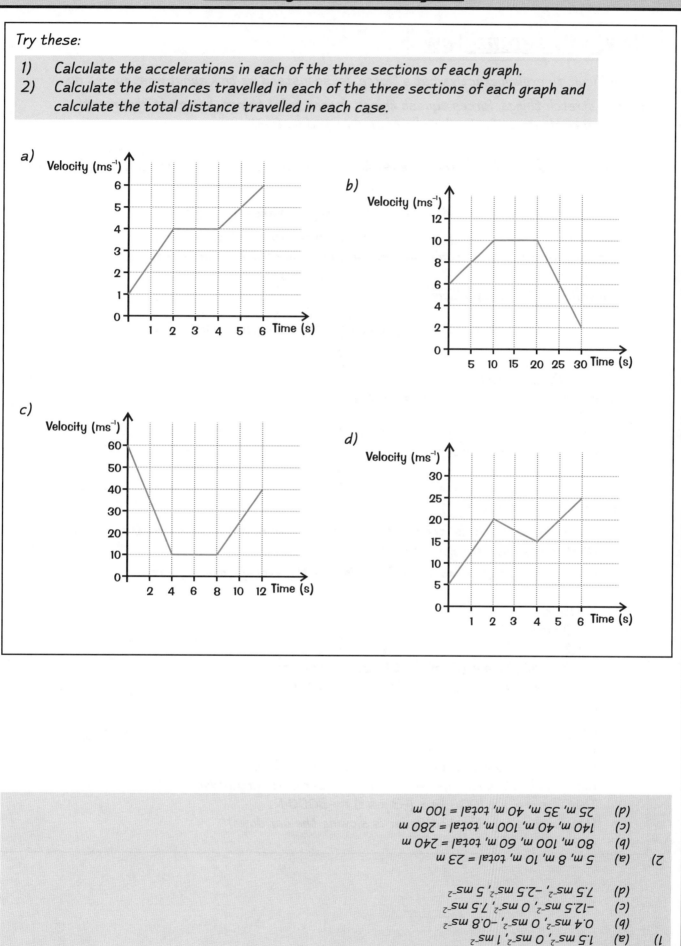

Forces and Acceleration

Newton's Second Law

It's difficult to explain exactly what a "force" is, so instead we talk about what forces do.

Forces stretch things, forces squash things, forces twist things, but most importantly, forces make things go faster (or slower or change direction).

When a resultant force (see page 14) acts on an object it changes the velocity of the object.

In other words, applying a resultant force to an object makes it <u>accelerate</u>.

This acceleration is <u>directly proportional</u> to the force. This just means that, for the same object, if you double the force applied, you double its acceleration.

We can write down this equation:

Force (N) = mass of object (kg) × acceleration of object (ms^{-2})

Or, in symbols:

$$F = m \times a$$

This is <u>Newton's second law of motion</u>.

Have a look at this example:

a) A car of mass 1000 kg accelerates uniformly from rest to 15 ms^{-1} in 20 s. What is the force accelerating it?

b) The car then stops suddenly in 5 s. What is the average braking force?

a) $v = 15\ ms^{-1}$
       $u = 0\ ms^{-1}$
       $t = 20\ s$
       $a = (v - u)/t$, so $a = (15\ ms^{-1} - 0) / 20\ s = 0.75\ ms^{-2}$.
       Then $F = m \times a = 1000\ kg \times 0.75\ ms^{-2} = 750\ N$.

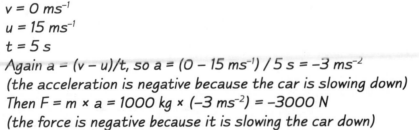

b) $v = 0\ ms^{-1}$
       $u = 15\ ms^{-1}$
       $t = 5\ s$
       Again $a = (v - u)/t$, so $a = (0 - 15\ ms^{-1}) / 5\ s = -3\ ms^{-2}$
       (the acceleration is negative because the car is slowing down)
       Then $F = m \times a = 1000\ kg \times (-3\ ms^{-2}) = -3000\ N$
       (the force is negative because it is slowing the car down)

Forces and Acceleration

Finding the Force When Given the Mass and the Acceleration

Try these (they're like the example on page 12):

1) A bus of mass 10 000 kg accelerates at 0.25 ms^{-2}. What is the force acting on it?
2) A car pulls a caravan of mass 800 kg. If it accelerates at 0.4 ms^{-2}, what force must the caravan experience?
3) An apple of mass 0.1 kg falls with acceleration of 9.8 ms^{-2}.
   What is the gravitational force pulling it down (its weight)?

Finding the Acceleration When Given the Force and the Mass

Example:
   What would be the acceleration of a 500 g mass if a force of 10 N acted on it?

   F = m × a. Dividing both sides by m gives F/m = a, so a = F/m = 10 N / 0.5 kg = 20 ms^{-2}.

Now try these questions:

4) What would be the initial acceleration of an arrow of mass 0.3 kg shot from a bow if the force from the bow-string is 200 N?
5) What would be the acceleration of a train of mass 10 000 kg if the force from the engine is 8000 N?
6) What would be the initial acceleration of a bullet fired from a rifle if the bullet has a mass of 0.008 kg and the force accelerating it is 2000 N?

Finding the Mass When Given the Acceleration and the Force

Consider this example:
   What is the mass of an object if a force of 250 N produces an acceleration of 2 ms^{-2}?

   F = m × a. Dividing both sides by a gives F/a = m, so m = F/a = 250 N / (2 ms^{-2}) = 125 kg

Now try these questions:

7) What is the mass of a sailing boat if a force of 120 N produces an acceleration of 0.5 ms^{-2}?
8) What is the mass of a ship if a force of 50 000 N produces an acceleration of 0.2 ms^{-2}?
9) What is the mass of a box if a force of 50 N produces an acceleration of 8 ms^{-2}?

Answers
1) 2500 N   6) 2.5 × 10^5 ms^{-2}
2) 320 N   7) 240 kg
3) 0.98 N   8) 2.5 × 10^5 kg
4) 667 ms^{-2} 9) 6.25 kg
5) 0.8 ms^{-2}

Balanced and Unbalanced Forces

Balanced and Unbalanced Forces

Force is a <u>vector</u>, just like displacement or velocity.

When more than one force acts on a body, you can add them together in just the same way as you add displacements or velocities.

You find the resultant force by putting the arrows "tip-to-tail".

If the resultant force is zero, the forces are <u>balanced</u>.

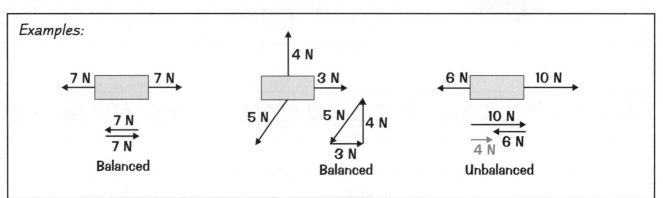

Examples:

Balanced

Balanced

Unbalanced

If there's a resultant force, then the forces are <u>unbalanced</u>
— there is a <u>net force</u> on the object.

Example:

A force of 10 newtons to the right and a force of 6 newtons to the left result in a net force of 4 newtons to the right. If these forces acted on an object of mass 5 kilograms it would produce an acceleration given by:

$$a = F/m = 4\,N\,/\,5\,kg = 0.8\ ms^{-2}$$

Have a go at these:

Work out the net forces on these objects and calculate the acceleration they would cause:

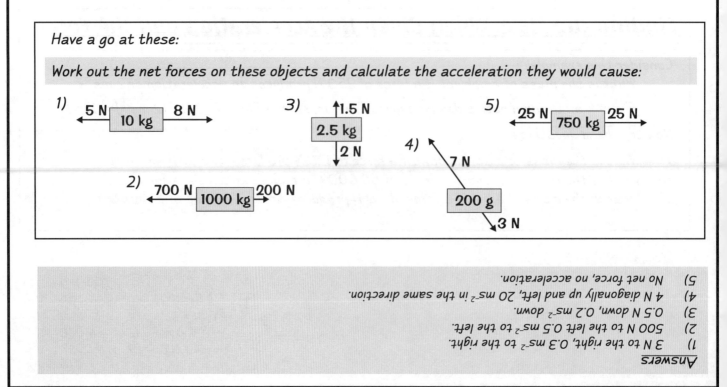

Kinetic and Gravitational Potential Energy

Kinetic Energy

Energy is a curious thing. You can't pick it up and look at it.

One thing's for certain though — if you're moving then you have energy.

This movement energy is more properly known as kinetic energy, and there's a formula for working it out:

> If a body of mass m (in kilograms) is moving with speed v (in metres per second) then its kinetic energy (in joules) is given by:
>
> kinetic energy = ½ × mass × speed^2

Or, in symbols:

$$E_k = \text{½} \times m \times v^2$$

Have a look at the following examples, and then try the questions after them.

Examples:

1) A car of mass 800 kg is travelling with a speed of 20 ms^{-1}.
   What is its kinetic energy?
   $E_k = \text{½} \times m \times v^2$, so $E_k = \text{½} \times 800 \text{ kg} \times (20 \text{ ms}^{-1})^2 = \text{½} \times 800 \text{ kg} \times 400 \text{ m}^2\text{s}^{-2}$
   $= 1.6 \times 10^5 \text{ J}$.

2) A ball has a speed of 2.5 ms^{-1} and has kinetic energy equal to 0.8 J.
   What is the mass of the ball?
   $E_k = \text{½} \times m \times v^2$. Multiplying both sides by 2 gives $2 \times E_k = m \times v^2$, then dividing both sides
   by v^2 gives $(2 \times E_k)/v^2 = m$, so $m = (2 \times E_k)/v^2 = (2 \times 0.8 \text{ J}) / (2.5 \text{ ms}^{-1})^2$
   $= 1.6 \text{ J} / (6.25 \text{ m}^2\text{s}^{-2}) = 0.256 \text{ kg}$

3) A bullet has kinetic energy equal to 1200 J. If its mass is 0.01 kg, what is its speed?
   From example 2) $2 \times E_k = m \times v^2$. Dividing both sides by m gives $(2 \times E_k)/m = v^2$, then taking
   square roots of both sides gives $\sqrt{((2 \times E_k)/m)} = v$,
   so $v = \sqrt{((2 \times E_k)/m)} = \sqrt{((2 \times 1200 \text{ J}) / 0.01 \text{ kg})} = 490 \text{ ms}^{-1}$ (to the nearest ms^{-1}).

Now try these questions:

1) An arrow of mass 0.4 kg is travelling at a speed of 80 ms^{-1}.
   What is its kinetic energy?

2) A ship has kinetic energy equal to 6×10^7 J when moving at 15 ms^{-1}. What is its mass?

3) A snail of mass 0.05 kg has a kinetic energy of 1×10^{-6} J. What is its speed?

Kinetic and Gravitational Potential Energy

Gravitational Potential Energy

When an object falls, its speed increases. As its speed increases, so does its kinetic energy.

Where does it get this energy from?

Answer: from the gravitational potential energy it had before it fell:

If a body of mass m (in kilograms) is raised through a height h (in metres) the gravitational potential energy (in joules) it gains is given by:

gravitational potential energy (J) = mass (kg) × gravitational field strength (Nkg⁻¹) × height (m)

So, in symbols it reads:

$$E_p = m \times g \times h$$

where the gravitational field strength is the ratio of an object's weight to its mass (in newtons per kilogram). It is given the symbol g, and at the surface of the Earth has an approximate value of 9.8 Nkg⁻¹.

Examples:

1) An 80 kilogram person in a lift is raised 45 metres. Assuming g = 9.8 Nkg⁻¹, what is the increase in gravitational potential energy?
$E_p = mgh$, so E_p = 80 kg × 9.8 Nkg⁻¹ × 45 m = 35 280 J

2) A mass raised 10 metres gains gravitational potential energy equal to 50 joules. What is that mass?
$E_p = mgh$. Dividing both sides by gh gives $E_p/gh = m$,
so m = E_p/gh = 50 J / (9.8 Nkg⁻¹ × 10 m) = 0.51 kg.

3) 600 kilograms of bricks are given 29 400 joules of gravitational potential energy. Through what height have they been raised?
$E_p = mgh$. Dividing both sides by mg gives $E_p/mg = h$,
so h = E_p/mg = 29 400 J / (600 kg × 9.8 Nkg⁻¹) = 5 m.

Now try these questions:

1) How much more gravitational potential energy does a 750 kilogram car have at the top of a 300 metre than at the bottom of the hill?

2) What mass, when raised through 7 metres, gains gravitational potential energy equal to 1715 joules?

3) A 60 kilogram person gains 24 696 joules of gravitational potential energy. How high have they climbed?

Answers
1) 2.205 × 10⁶ J or 2.205 MJ
2) 25 kg
3) 42 m

Kinetic and Gravitational Potential Energy

The Conservation of Energy Applied to Falling Bodies

The principle of <u>conservation of energy</u> states that:

"Energy cannot be created or destroyed — it can only converted into other forms"

So as long as you ignore air resistance...

...for a <u>falling</u> object:

Kinetic Energy Gained (in joules) = Gravitational Potential Energy Lost (in joules)

...and for an object <u>thrown</u> or <u>catapulted</u> upwards:

Gravitational Potential Energy Gained (in joules) = Kinetic Energy Lost (in joules)

This can be very useful in solving problems.
Read through the examples and then have a go at the questions afterwards.
(In all the questions, you can ignore air resistance.)

Examples:

1) An apple of mass 0.1 kilograms falls from a tree of height 2 metres.
   With what speed does it hit the ground? Give your answer to 2 decimal places.

   E_p lost = mgh = 0.1 kg × 9.8 Nkg^{-1} × 2 m = 1.96 J
   Therefore E_k gained = 1.96 J, so E_k = ½ × m × v² = 1.96 J.
   From page 15, v = $\sqrt{(2 × E_k)/m}$, so v = $\sqrt{(2 × 1.96 J)/0.1 kg}$ = 6.26 ms^{-1}

2) A ball of mass 0.2 kilograms is thrown upwards at 10 metres per second.
   How high does it get?

   E_k lost = ½ × m × v² = ½ × 0.2 kg × (10 ms^{-1})² = 10 J.
   Therefore, E_p gained = 10 J, so E_p = mgh = 10 J.
   From page 16, h = E_p/mg, so h = 10 J / (0.2 kg × 9.8 Nkg^{-1}) = 5.10 m.

Now try these (give your answers to 3 significant figures):

1) A book of mass 0.5 kilograms falls off a table top 1 metre from the floor. With what speed is it travelling when it lands?

2) A bullet of mass 0.01 kilograms is fired upwards at 400 ms^{-1}. What height does it reach?

Work

Work — the Amount of Energy a Force Gives an Object

When you push an object you can increase its energy by:

1) Pushing it up hill,
2) Accelerating it,
3) Doing both at once.

In any case, the amount of energy (in joules) that a force gives an object is called the work done, and can be calculated using the formula:

Work Done by a Force = Size of Force × Distance Moved in the Direction of the Force
(in joules)   (in newtons)   While the Force is Acting (in metres)

Or, in symbols: $W = F \times d$

Examples:

1) A 5 newton force to the north pushes an object 3 metres in the same direction.
   What is the work done?
   $W = F \times d$, so $W = 5\,N \times 3\,m = 15\,J$.

2) A 10 newton force to the north pushes an object 15 metres in a north-easterly direction.
   What is the work done?
   N.B. You need to use trigonometry to find the distance travelled in the direction of the force (i.e. north).

   $d = 15 \cos 45° = 10.6\,m$
   So, $W = F \times d = 10\,N \times 10.6\,m = 106\,J$.

3) A force of 35 newtons north acts on an object as it moves 7 m in a westerly direction.
   What is the work done by the force?
   The object is moving at 90° to the force, so $d = 0\,m$.
   Therefore, $W = F \times d = 35\,N \times 0\,m = 0\,J$.

Have a go at these questions:

1) A force of 25 newtons to the west moves an object 40 metres in the same direction.
   What is the work done?
2) A force of 10 newtons to the north-east acts on an object as it moves 25 metres to the south-east. What is the work done by the force?
3) A force of 3 newtons to the west acts on an object as it moves 10 metres to the south-west. What is the work done by the force?

Work

Work Done = Increase in Gravitational and Kinetic Energy

Here are three possible situations:

1) The work done goes <u>entirely into the gravitational potential energy</u> of an object.
   E.g. if you are lifting an object straight upwards.

   Work done = force × distance

   = weight of object × height lifted

   = mass of object × gravitational field strength × height

   So: <u>work done = mgh = the increase in gravitational energy</u>

2) The work done goes <u>entirely into the kinetic energy</u> of an object.
   E.g. if a 5 newton force acts on a 3 kilogram body over a distance of 10 metres, what is its final speed if it was initially at rest?

   Work done = increase in kinetic energy

   $F × d = ½ × m × v^2$. Dividing both sides by m gives:

   $(F × d)/m = ½ × v^2$. Multiplying both sides by 2 gives:

   $2 × (F × d)/m = v^2$. Finally, taking the square root of both sides gives:

   $v = √(2 × (F × d)/m) = √(2 × (5 N × 10 m) / 3 kg) = \underline{5.8\ ms^{-1}}$

3) The work done goes into increasing <u>both the kinetic and the gravitational energy</u>.

   Work done = increase in E_k + increase in E_p

   $F × d = ½ × m × v^2 + mgh$

Work done can also go into increasing the elastic potential energy of something (if you stretch or squash it).

Have a go at these questions:

1) A 100 newton force lifts a 5 kilogram object 2 metres. When the force is removed, the object continues to move upwards. Calculate: (a) the work done by the force; (b) the gain in gravitational potential energy (using g = 9.8 Nkg⁻¹); (c) the gain in kinetic energy.

2) A 10 newton force pushes an object of mass 2 kilograms horizontally on a frictionless surface for 25 metres. Calculate: (a) the work done; (b) the final speed of the object if it was initially at rest.

Answers
1) (a) 200 J
   (b) 98 J
   (c) 102 J
2) (a) 250 J
   (b) 15.8 ms⁻¹

Power

Power — the Work Done Every Second

In mechanical situations, whenever energy is converted, work is being done.

For example, when an object is falling, the force of gravity is doing work on that object equal to the increase in kinetic energy (ignoring air resistance).

The rate at which this work is being done is called the <u>power</u>.

You can calculate it using:

> Power (in watts) = Work Done (in joules) / Time Taken (in seconds)

Or, in symbols:

$$P = W / t$$

No one dared suggest Rhona had PWt

Consider the following examples:

1) If 10 joules of work is done in 2 seconds, what is the power?

   $P = W/t = 10 \text{ J} / 2 \text{ s} = 5 \text{ W}$.

2) A force of 100 newtons pushes an object 5 metres in 4 seconds. What is the power? (Assume the motion is in the same direction as the force.)

   $W = F \times d = 100 \text{ N} \times 5 \text{ m} = 500 \text{ J}$

   $P = W/t = 500 \text{ J} / 4 \text{ s} = 125 \text{ W}$.

3) For how long must a 5 kilowatt (5000 watt) engine run to do 200 kilojoules (2×10^5 joules) of work?

   $P = W/t$. Multiplying both sides by t gives $P \times t = W$, then dividing both sides by P gives: $t = W/P$.

   So, $t = W/P = 2 \times 10^5 \text{ J} / 5000 \text{ W} = 40 \text{ s}$.

Try these:

1) If a lift mechanism works at 15 kilowatts, how long does it take to do 100 kilojoules of work?

2) What is the power output of a motor if it does 250 joules of work in 4 seconds?

3) If a force of 200 newtons pushes an object 1.5 kilometres in a minute, at what power is it working? (Assume the motion is in the same direction as the force.)

Answers
1) 6.7 s
2) 62.5 W
3) 5000 W

Power

The Power Developed by a Moving Force

There's a useful equation you can derive for the work done by a force every second on a <u>moving</u> object. Follow through the working below:

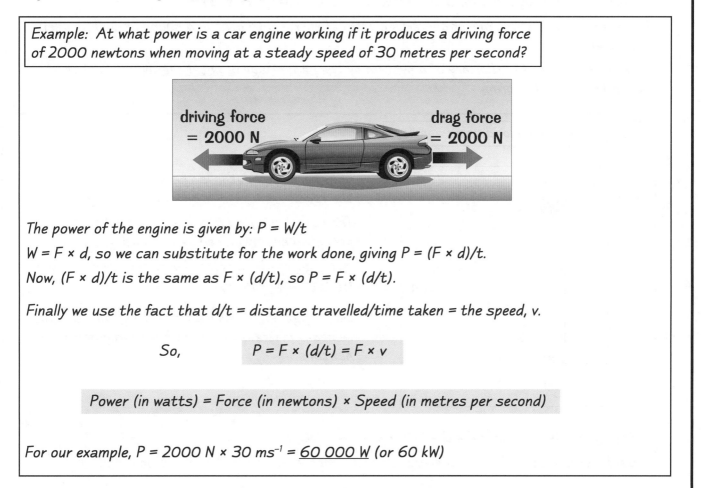

Example: At what power is a car engine working if it produces a driving force of 2000 newtons when moving at a steady speed of 30 metres per second?

driving force = 2000 N

drag force = 2000 N

The power of the engine is given by: $P = W/t$

$W = F \times d$, so we can substitute for the work done, giving $P = (F \times d)/t$.

Now, $(F \times d)/t$ is the same as $F \times (d/t)$, so $P = F \times (d/t)$.

Finally we use the fact that d/t = distance travelled/time taken = the speed, v.

So, $\qquad P = F \times (d/t) = F \times v$

Power (in watts) = Force (in newtons) × Speed (in metres per second)

For our example, $P = 2000 \text{ N} \times 30 \text{ ms}^{-1} = \underline{60\ 000 \text{ W}}$ (or 60 kW)

<u>IMPORTANT</u>:
The formula $P = Fv$ is <u>only</u> true when the object is moving at a <u>constant velocity</u> in the <u>same direction as the force</u>.

Have a go at these:

1) What is the power developed by a train engine if its driving force of 1.8×10^5 newtons produces a constant speed of 40 metres per second?

2) A skydiver is falling at a terminal velocity of 45 metres per second. If her weight is 700 newtons, at what rate is gravity doing work on her?

Efficiency

How Much of What You Put In Do You Get Out?

For most mechanical systems you put in energy in one form and it gives out energy in another.

However, some energy is always converted into forms that aren't useful.

For example, an electric motor converts electrical energy into heat and sound as well as useful kinetic energy.

You can measure the efficiency of a system by the <u>percentage of total energy put in that is converted to useful forms</u>.

Example: Raising a load using a pulley

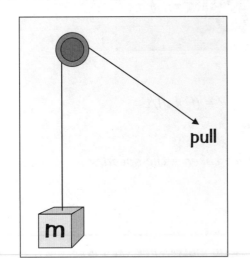

The <u>energy you put in</u> is the work you do pulling the rope.

The <u>useful energy out</u> is the gravitational potential energy gained by the load.

Some energy is converted into heat and sound by <u>friction</u> at the pulley.

Say the mass of the load is 10 kilograms and it's raised 5 metres. You pull with a force of 120 newtons.

(Take g = 9.8 Nkg⁻¹.)

Energy in = Work done = F × d = 120 N × 5 m = <u>600 J</u>

Useful energy out = Potential energy gained = mgh = 10 kg × 9.8 Nkg⁻¹ × 5 m = <u>490 J</u>

Efficiency = (Useful energy out / Total energy in) × 100%

= (490/600) × 100% = <u>81.7%</u>

Have a go at these questions:

1) A motor uses 300 joules of electrical energy in lifting a 10 kilogram mass through 2 metres. What is its efficiency? (Take g = 9.8 Nkg⁻¹.)

2) It takes 800 kilojoules (8 × 10⁵ joules) of chemical energy from the petrol in a car engine to accelerate a 500 kilogram vehicle from rest to 20 metres per second on a flat road:
(a) What is the gain in kinetic energy?
(b) What is the efficiency of the car?

Charge

Some Particles Have a Property Called Charge

Some particles (in fact, most fundamental particles) have a property called charge. It's measured in coulombs, symbol C. This charge can be either positive or negative, and the force between charged particles can be an attraction or a repulsion.

This force is called the electrostatic force and has the following properties:

1) Particles with _opposite_ charges _attract_ each other.

2) Particles with the _same_ charge _repel_ each other.

3) The force is bigger if the sizes of the charges (in coulombs) are bigger, or if the particles are closer together.

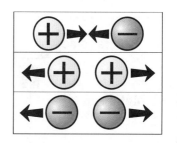

Have a look at these worked examples.

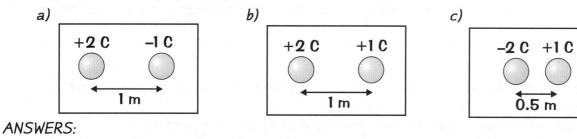
QUESTIONS:
1) Which of these pairs of particles attract and which repel?
2) Between which pair is the electrostatic force greatest?

a)

+2 C   −1 C

⟷ 1 m

b)

+2 C   +1 C

⟷ 1 m

c)

−2 C +1 C

⟷ 0.5 m

ANSWERS:
1) a) attract; b) repel; c) attract
2) c), because they all have the same sized charges, but these are closer together.

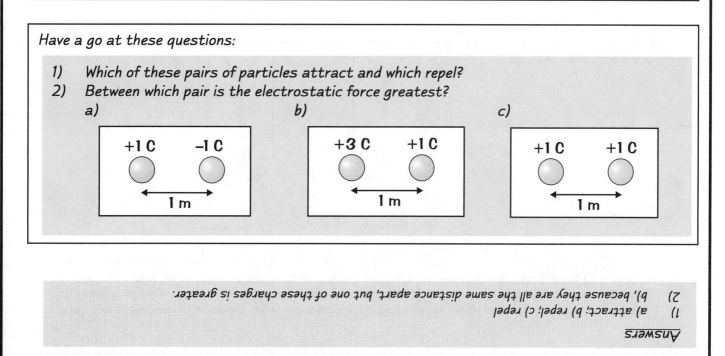
Have a go at these questions:

1) Which of these pairs of particles attract and which repel?
2) Between which pair is the electrostatic force greatest?

a)

+1 C   −1 C

⟷ 1 m

b)

+3 C   +1 C

⟷ 1 m

c)

+1 C   +1 C

⟷ 1 m

Charge

Detecting Charge: The Gold-Leaf Electroscope

1) The basic components of a gold-leaf electroscope are a metal disc connected to a metal rod, at the bottom of which are attached two thin pieces of gold leaf.

2) When a charged object is pulled firmly across the disc, electrons flow to try to neutralise the object. This leaves the disc with too many or too few electrons. The charge then spreads through the metal rod to the gold leaves. Since like charges repel, the gold leaves rise.

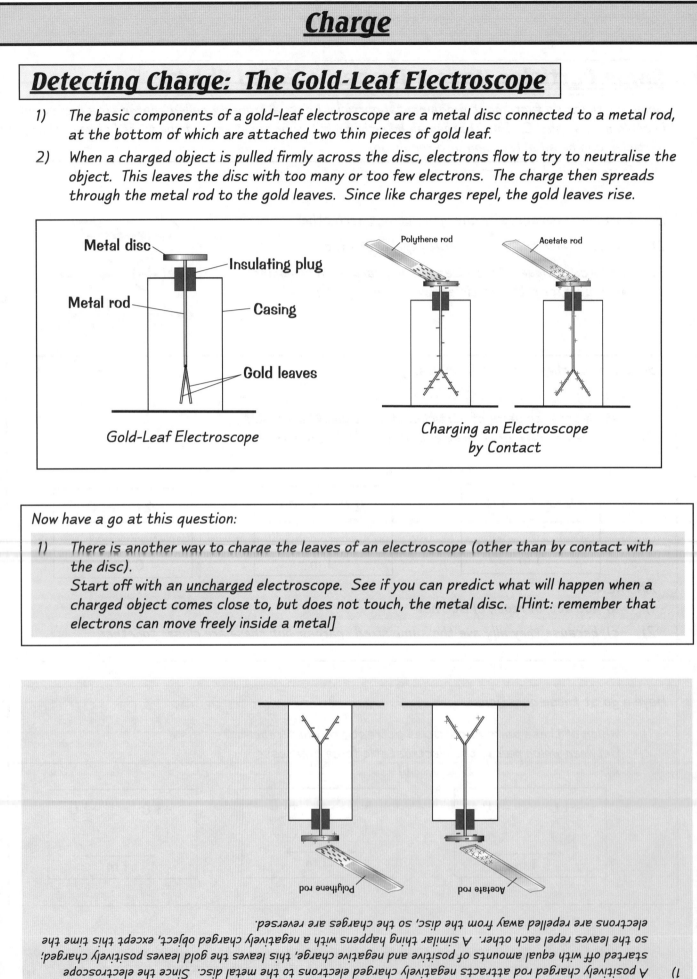

Gold-Leaf Electroscope

Charging an Electroscope by Contact

Now have a go at this question:

1) There is another way to charge the leaves of an electroscope (other than by contact with the disc).
Start off with an <u>uncharged</u> electroscope. See if you can predict what will happen when a charged object comes close to, but does not touch, the metal disc. [Hint: remember that electrons can move freely inside a metal]

Current

Electric Current — The Flow of Charge

If you connect a wire to a battery, negatively charged electrons flow through
the wire from the negative end of the battery to the positive end. This flow of charge is
an electric current, and, as you know, the charge will only flow if there's a complete circuit.

The electric current at a point in the wire can be defined as:

Current = the amount of charge passing the point / the time it takes for the charge to pass
(in amps)   (in coulombs)   (in seconds)

Or, equivalently, as the amount of charge passing the point per second.

In symbols you can write this as:

$$I = \Delta Q / \Delta t$$

The "Δ" sign is a capital Greek "delta", and just means "the change in".

Here are a few examples:

1) 6 coulombs of charge flow through a lamp in one minute.
   What is the current through the lamp?
   $I = \Delta Q / \Delta t$, so $I = 6\ C / 60\ s = 0.1\ A$

2) There is a current of 2 amps in a wire. How much charge will flow in 5 minutes?
   $I = \Delta Q / \Delta t$. Multiplying both sides by Δt gives $I \times \Delta t = \Delta Q$, so $\Delta Q = 2\ A \times 300\ s = 600\ C$

3) There is a current of 0.5 amps through a resistor.
   How long does it take for 0.1 coulombs to pass through it?
   From example 2, $I \times \Delta t = \Delta Q$. Dividing both sides by I gives $\Delta t = \Delta Q / I$,
   so $\Delta t = 0.1\ C / 0.5\ A = 0.2\ s$

Now have a go at these:

1) There is a current of 0.2 amps at a point in a circuit. How much charge will flow past that
   point in 2 minutes?
2) 0.01 coulombs of charge flows through a wire in 20 seconds. What is the current?
3) There is a current of 0.005 amps through a lamp. How long does it take for 1 coulomb of
   charge to pass through it?

Answers
1) 24 C
2) $5 \times 10^{-4}\ A$ (or 0.5 mA)
3) 200 s (or 3 min 20 s)

Current

What Happens When an Electric Current Meets a Junction?

You can easily build a circuit in which the electric
current has a choice about which wire to travel down —
two lamps connected in parallel is a good example.

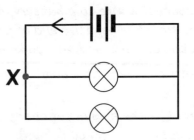

At point "X" the current from the power supply can go
down either of two possible routes. How much goes down
each wire depends on the resistances of each route, but
one thing is for certain:

> The total amount of charge leaving the junction every second
> is the same as the total amount entering it every second.

Or, more concisely:

> The sum of the currents going into the junction = the sum of the currents going out.

This is a simplified statement of <u>Kirchhoff's first rule</u>.

The following examples each have one unknown current.
You can find the unknown current using Kirchhoff's first rule:

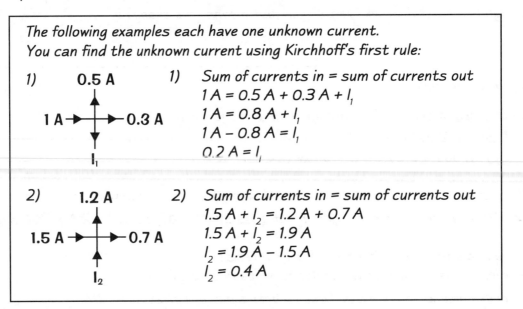

1)

1) Sum of currents in = sum of currents out
$1\,A = 0.5\,A + 0.3\,A + I_1$
$1\,A = 0.8\,A + I_1$
$1\,A - 0.8\,A = I_1$
$0.2\,A = I_1$

2)

2) Sum of currents in = sum of currents out
$1.5\,A + I_2 = 1.2\,A + 0.7\,A$
$1.5\,A + I_2 = 1.9\,A$
$I_2 = 1.9\,A - 1.5\,A$
$I_2 = 0.4\,A$

Try some for yourself:

Find the unknown currents:

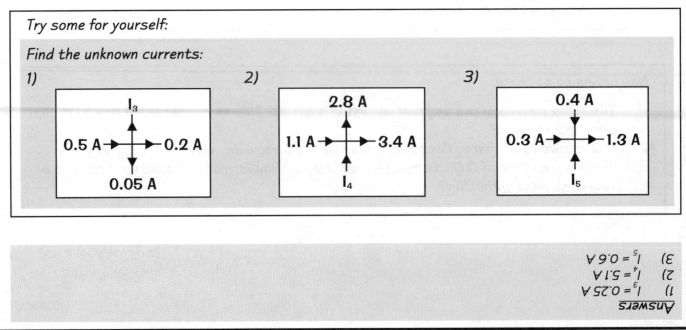

1)

2)

3)

Potential Difference

Potential Difference (Voltage) — Energy Per Unit Charge

In any circuit energy is transferred from the power supply to the components (lamps, motors etc.), where it's converted into other forms, e.g. light. This energy is carried around the circuit by the charged particles. If you think about one coulomb of charge flowing around a circuit then:

(a) The amount of energy it's given by the power supply is the voltage across the power supply.
(b) The amount of energy it gives to each individual component in the circuit is the voltage across that component.

In other words, the voltage, or potential difference, across a component is the amount of energy (in joules) that it converts for every coulomb of charge that passes through it.

> Voltage across component = Energy converted / Charge that passes through it
>   (in volts)   (in joules)   (in coulombs)

Or, in symbols: $V = E/Q$

Here are a few examples:

1) A lamp gives out 10 joules of energy when 0.5 coulombs pass through it.
    What is the potential difference across the lamp?

    $V = E/Q = 10\ J / 0.5\ C = 20\ V$

2) What is the maximum amount of energy an electric heater could produce at 200 volts if the amount of charge that passes through it is 10 coulombs?

    $V = E/Q$. Multiplying both sides by Q gives $V \times Q = E$, so $E = 200\ V \times 10\ C = 2000\ J$

3) How much charge has passed through a 12 volt motor if the energy it has converted is 3 joules?
    From example 2, $V \times Q = E$
    Dividing both sides by V gives $Q = E/V$, so $Q = 3\ J / 12\ V = 0.25\ C$

Have a go at these problems:

1) What is the maximum amount of energy that a lamp could give out if the voltage across it is 6 volts and the amount of charge that passes through it is 0.5 coulombs?
2) How much charge has passed through a circuit if 100 joules of energy have been converted across a potential difference of 8 volts?
3) An electric motor converts 1 joule of energy when 0.04 coulombs of charge pass through it. What is the potential difference across the motor?

Answers
1)   3 J
2)   12.5 C
3)   25 V

Energy in Electrical Circuits

Conservation of Energy in Electrical Circuits

Energy is given to charged particles by the power supply and taken off them by the components in the circuit. Since energy is conserved, the amount of energy one coulomb of charge loses when going around the circuit must be equal to the energy it's given by the power supply.

And more than that, this must be true _regardless_ of the route the charge takes around the circuit. So, you can say that:

> For any closed loop in a circuit the sum of the potential differences across the components equals the voltage of the power supply.

This is a case of _Kirchhoff's second rule_.

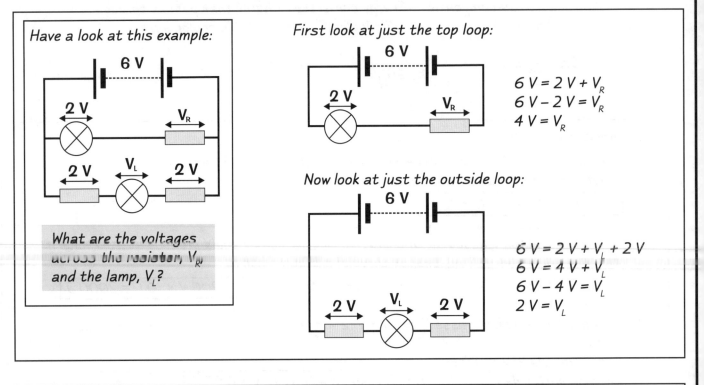

Have a look at this example:

6 V

2 V V_R

2 V V_L 2 V

What are the voltages across the resistor, V_R, and the lamp, V_L?

First look at just the top loop:

6 V

2 V V_R

$6 V = 2 V + V_R$
$6 V - 2 V = V_R$
$4 V = V_R$

Now look at just the outside loop:

6 V

2 V V_L 2 V

$6 V = 2 V + V_L + 2 V$
$6 V = 4 V + V_L$
$6 V - 4 V = V_L$
$2 V = V_L$

Now you do this one:

For the circuit on the right, calculate:

(a)   the voltage across the motor, V_M

(b)   the voltage across the loudspeaker, V_S

12 V

V_M — M   3 V

6 V   2 V V_S

Resistance

Resistance — The Ratio of Voltage / Current

Generally speaking, when there's a voltage across a component there'll be a current through it. Usually, as the voltage is increased the current increases — this makes sense if you think of the voltage as a kind of force pushing the charged particles. You can formalise the relationship between current and voltage by defining "*resistance*":

> Resistance of a component = Voltage across it / Current passing through it
> (in ohms)   (in volts)   (in amps)

Or, in symbols:

$$R = V / I$$

Multiplying both sides by I gives:

$$V = I \times R$$

Ed got in there while Lucy's resistance was low...

Components with a *low resistance* allow a *large* current to flow through them, while components with a *high resistance* allow only a *small* current. The resistance isn't usually a constant though — it can take different values as the current and voltage change, or it can change with conditions like temperature and light level.

Here are some examples:

1) If a potential difference of 12 volts across a component causes a current of 0.001 amps to flow, what is the resistance?

    $R = V/I$, so $R = 12\ V / 0.001\ A = 12\ 000\ \Omega$, or $12\ k\Omega$

2) If a current of 0.2 amps passes through a resistance of 200 ohms, what is the voltage?

    $V = I \times R$, so $V = 0.2\ A \times 200\ \Omega = 40\ V$

3) What current will flow through a resistance of 800 ohms if the voltage across it is 6 volts?

    $V = I \times R$. Dividing both sides by R gives $I = V/R$, so $I = 6\ V / 800\ \Omega = 0.0075\ A$ (or $7.5\ mA$)

Here are some for you to do:

1) If a current of 2.5 amps passes through a component with a resistance of 10 ohms, what is the voltage?
2) What current will flow through a resistance of 2500 ohms if the voltage across it is 6 volts?
3) What is the resistance of a component if 1.5 volts drives a current of 0.02 amps through it?

Answers

1) 25 V
2) 0.0024 A or 2.4 mA
3) 75 Ω

Resistance

Voltage-Current Graphs

Look at the following graphs showing the current through different components as the voltage across them is changed (negative values refer to charges flowing the other way):

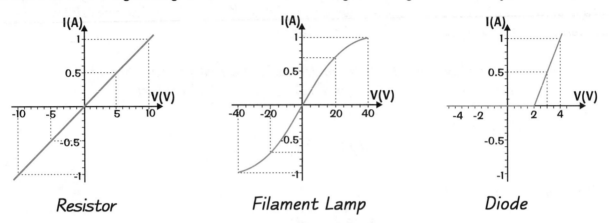

Resistor	Filament Lamp	Diode

We can use the graphs to determine the resistance at different voltages as follows:

Example:
What is the resistance of the <u>resistor</u> at:
(a) –10 V?
(b) –5 V?
(c) 5 V?
(d) 10 V?

(a) R = V/I = –10 V / –1 A = 10 Ω
(b) R = V/I = –5 V / –0.5 A = 10 Ω
(c) R = V/I = 5 V / 0.5 A = 10 Ω
(d) R = V/I = 10 V / 1 A = 10 Ω

Now you have a go at the other two:

1) What is the resistance of the <u>filament lamp</u> at:
(a) 10 V?
(b) 20 V?
(c) 30 V?
(d) 40 V?

2) What is the resistance of the <u>diode</u> at:
(a) 1 V?
(b) 2 V?
(c) 3 V?
(d) 4 V?

Power in Circuits

Power — The Energy Converted Every Second

Components in electrical circuits convert the energy carried by electrons into other forms.
The amount of energy, in joules, that's converted every second is the <u>power</u> of that component:

> Power (in watts) = Amount of Energy Converted (in joules) / Time Taken (in seconds)

Or, in symbols:

$$P = E / t$$

The energy converted is equal to the voltage across the component x the amount of charge that has flowed through it ($E = V \times Q$) — see p27.

So: $\boxed{P = V \times Q / t}$

and the amount of charge that flows through a component is equal to the current through it x the time taken ($Q = I \times t$)

So: $\boxed{P = V \times I \times t / t}$

Cancelling the "t"s gives: $\boxed{P = V \times I}$

> Power (in watts) = Voltage Across Component (in volts) x Current Through Component (in amps)

Here are some examples:

1) A lift motor converts 3×10^5 joules of electrical energy into gravitational potential energy in a single one-minute journey. At what power is it working?

$\boxed{P = E/t, \text{ so } P = 3 \times 10^5 \text{ J} / 60 \text{ s} = 5000 \text{ W (or 5 kW)}.}$

2) If the voltage across a component is 6 volts and the current through it is 0.5 milliamps (5×10^{-4} amps), at what rate is it converting electrical energy to other forms?

$\boxed{P = I \times V, \text{ so } P = 5 \times 10^{-4} \text{ A} \times 6 \text{ V} = 0.003 \text{ W (or 3 mW)}.}$

3) If a 12 watt lamp has a current through it of 1.5 amps, what is the voltage across it?

$\boxed{P = I \times V. \text{ Dividing both sides by I gives } V = P/I, \text{ so } V = 12 \text{ W} / 1.5 \text{ A} = 8 \text{ V}.}$

Have a go at these questions:

1) What is the power output of a component if the current through it is 0.12 amps when the voltage across it is 6 volts?
2) What current passes through a 40 watt heater when the voltage across it is 10 volts?
3) How much electrical energy would be converted by the 40 watt heater in 10 seconds?

Answers
1) 0.72 W
2) 4 A
3) 400 J

Power in Circuits

Power — More Equations

You can combine the last equation for the power of an electrical component, $P = V \times I$, with the resistance equation (see p29) to create two more useful equations.

First, replace V with I x R to give:

$$P = I \times R \times I = I^2R$$

Power (in watts) = [Current (in amps)]^2 × Resistance (in ohms)

Second, replace I with V/R to give:

$$P = V \times V/R = V^2/R$$

Power (in watts) = [Voltage (in volts)]^2 / Resistance (in ohms)

Here are some examples — the key here is choosing the right equation to use. If the question gives you the value of two variables and asks you to find another, you should choose the equation that relates these three variables. You might have to rearrange it before using it.

1) What is the power output of a component of resistance 100 ohms if the current through it is 0.2 amps?

$P = I^2R$, so $\boxed{P = (0.2\ A)^2 \times 100\ \Omega = 4\ W.}$ (P = V^2/R wouldn't have been any use here.)

2) How much energy is converted in 10 s if the voltage is 100 V and the resistance is 5000 Ω?

$P = V^2/R$, so $P = 100^2/5000 = 2$ W. But power is the energy converted per second, so the energy converted in 10 s is $\boxed{2\ W \times 10\ s = 20\ J.}$ (P = I^{2}R wouldn't have helped much.)

3) Resistors get hotter when a current flows through them. If you double the current through a resistor, what happens to the amount of heat energy produced every second?

It increases by a factor of 4 — this is because the current is squared in the expression for the power (you can substitute some values of I and R in to check this).

4) If a lamp has a power rating of 6 W and the voltage across it is 12 V, what is its resistance?

You don't have an expression for the resistance so far, so you'll need to rearrange one. You need the equation that relates P, V and R, i.e. $P = V^2/R$.

Multiplying both sides by R gives $P \times R = V^2$, and dividing by P gives:

$$R = V^2/P,\ so\ \boxed{R = (12\ V)^2/6\ W = 24\ \Omega}$$

Now have a go at these:

1) What is the power output of a component of resistance 2000 ohms if the current through it is 1.2 amps?
2) How much energy is converted in 1 minute if the resistance is 100 Ω and the current is 2 A?
3) If a lamp has a power rating of 6 watts and the current through it is 0.5 amps, what is the resistance?

Answers: 1) 2880 W 2) 24 000 J, or 24 kJ 3) 24 Ω

Waves

What Are Waves?

1) Waves carry vibrations and energy from one place to another without transferring matter.
2) You can make waves using a slinky spring.
3) The energy you put in by shaking one end is transferred along the spring.

Transverse Waves

Transverse waves have vibrations at 90° to the direction of travel of the wave.

E.g. Shaking a slinky spring from side to side.

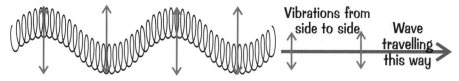

Vibrations from side to side

Wave travelling this way

Longitudinal Waves

Longitudinal waves have vibrations along the same direction as the wave is travelling.

E.g. Plucking a slinky spring.

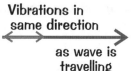

Vibrations in same direction as wave is travelling

Displacement-Distance Graphs

For any wave you can draw a graph to show how far each part of the wave is displaced from its equilibrium position for different distances along the wave, e.g. how far each turn of a slinky spring is displaced sideways as a transverse wave passes along the spring.

(The dashed line shows the displacement of each part of the wave a short time later.)

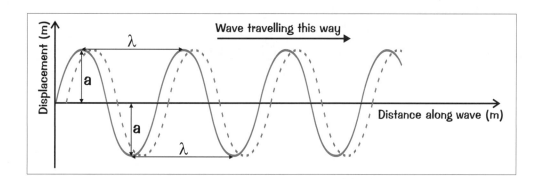

Wave travelling this way

Displacement (m)

Distance along wave (m)

λ
a
a
λ

Amplitude (symbol, a) = the furthest displacement of one part of the wave from its equilibrium position, measured in metres.

Wavelength (symbol, λ) = the shortest distance between two parts of the wave that are in the same stage of motion — in particular, the distance between adjacent peaks or troughs, measured in metres.

Waves

Displacement-Time Graphs

As well as looking at a "snapshot" of a whole wave (displacement-distance graphs) you can consider just one point on a wave and plot how its displacement changes with time.

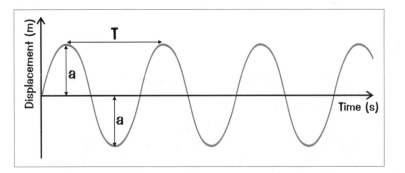

Time period (symbol, T) = the time for one complete oscillation of one point on the wave, measured in seconds.

Have a go at these questions:

1) Sketch a graph of the displacement against distance for two complete wavelengths of a wave of amplitude 0.2 metres and wavelength 1.5 metres.

2) Sketch a graph of the displacement against time for two complete oscillations of one part of a wave of amplitude 0.6 metres and time period 2 seconds.

3) Sketch a graph of the displacement against distance for five full wavelengths of a wave with amplitude 0.01 metres and wavelength 0.02 metres.

4) Sketch a graph of the displacement against time for five complete oscillations of one part of a wave of amplitude 0.05 metres and time period 0.8 seconds.

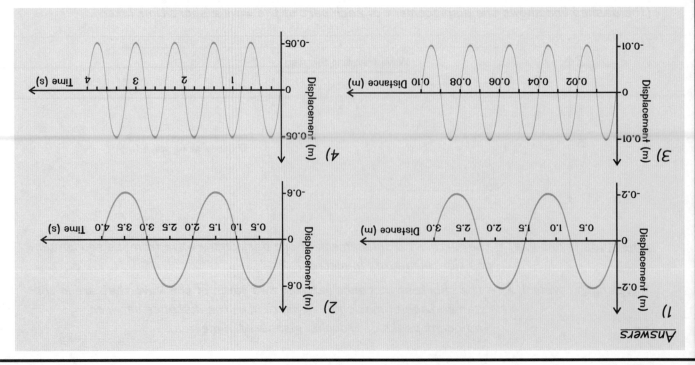

Answers

Frequency and Time Period

Frequency and Time Period

Consider one point on a wave.

If it has a time period of 0.2 seconds, i.e. it takes 0.2 seconds to complete one full oscillation, then in one second it will complete 5 full oscillations.

It has a _frequency_ of 5 hertz.

> The number of oscillations of one point on a wave every second is called the _frequency_ of the wave. It has the symbol f and is measured in hertz (symbol, Hz).

1) If you know the time period T you can work out the frequency using the equation f = 1/T.
2) If you know the frequency f you can work out the time period using the equation T = 1/f.

Examples:

1) One coil of a spring oscillates with a time period of 0.008 seconds. What is the frequency of the wave passing along that spring?

   f = 1/T = 1 / 0.008 s = 125 Hz

2) A wave has a frequency of 350 Hz. What is the period of oscillation of one point on that wave?

   T = 1/f = 1 / 350 Hz = 0.0029 s

Now you try these questions:

1) Ripples on the surface of a pond have a frequency of 12 Hz. What is the time period of oscillation of particles in the water?
2) One turn of a slinky spring takes 0.45 seconds to complete one full oscillation. What is the frequency of the wave on the spring?
3) A radio signal has a frequency of 8×10^5 Hz (800 kHz). What is the time period of oscillations of the electromagnetic field?
4) Oscillations in a sound wave have a time period of 0.002 seconds. What is the frequency of the sound?

The Wave Equation

The Wave Equation Relates Speed, Frequency and Wavelength

For a wave of frequency f (in hertz), wavelength λ (in metres) and wave speed v (in metres per second) the wave equation is:

$$v = f \times \lambda$$

In other words:

speed (ms⁻¹) = frequency (Hz) × wavelength (m)

Look at these examples of using the wave equation:

1) Sound is a longitudinal wave. If a sound has a frequency of 250 Hz and a wavelength of 1.32 metres, what is the speed of sound in air?

$v = f \times \lambda$, so v = 250 Hz × 1.32 m = 330 ms⁻¹

2) All electromagnetic waves travel at 3×10^8 ms⁻¹ in free space. If a radio signal has a wavelength of 1.5 kilometres, what is its frequency? (Hint: radio waves are a member of the electromagnetic spectrum.)

$v = f \times \lambda$. Dividing both sides by λ gives v/λ = f, so f = v/λ = (3×10^8 ms⁻¹) / 1500 m = 2×10^5 Hz = 200 kHz.

3) If a wave has speed 50 ms⁻¹ and frequency 0.8 Hz, what is the wavelength?

$v = f \times \lambda$. Dividing both sides by f gives v/f = λ, so λ = v/f = (50 ms⁻¹) / 0.8 Hz = 62.5 m.

Now have a go at these questions:

1) What is the frequency of a water wave of wavelength 0.4 metres and wave speed 0.7 ms⁻¹?

2) What is the wavelength of radio waves of frequency 1×10^8 Hz? (Hint: speed of electromagnetic waves in free space = 3×10^8 ms⁻¹.)

3) What is the speed of a wave of frequency 800 Hz and wavelength 2.5 metres?

4) What is the frequency of a sound wave of wavelength 0.25 metres? (Hint: speed of sound in air = 330 ms⁻¹.)

5) What is the speed of a wave along a spring if it has frequency 3 Hz and wavelength 1.4 metres?

6) What is the wavelength if the wave speed is 150 ms⁻¹ and the frequency is 600 Hz?

Reflection and Refraction

Reflection of Waves

When a wave hits a boundary between one medium and another, some (or nearly all) of the wave is reflected back.

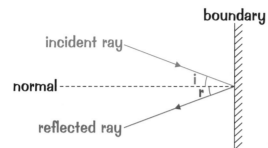

The <u>law of reflection</u> says that:

angle of incidence (i) = angle of reflection (r)

The angles of incidence and reflection are both measured from the normal — an imaginary line running perpendicular to the boundary.

Refraction of Waves

Reflection isn't all that happens when a wave meets a boundary. Usually, some of it is <u>refracted</u> too — it passes through the boundary and <u>changes direction</u>.

Waves travel at different speeds in different media. Electromagnetic waves, like light, usually travel slower in denser media.

If the wave hits the boundary 'face on', it slows down without changing direction.

If the wave hits at an angle, this bit slows down first...

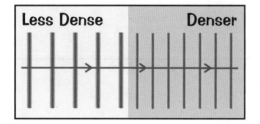 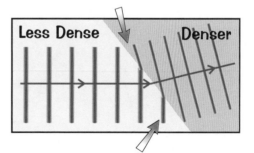

...while this bit carries on until it meets the boundary. The wave <u>changes direction</u>.

When an electromagnetic wave enters a <u>denser</u> medium, it bends <u>towards</u> the normal. And when it enters a <u>less dense</u> medium, it bends <u>away</u> from the normal.

More Questions on Waves

More questions to have a go at:

Below are graphs of displacement against distance along the wave and displacement of one part of the wave against time for two different waves. In each case:

(a) What is the amplitude of the wave?
(b) What is the wavelength of the wave?
(c) What is the time period?
(d) Calculate the frequency.
(e) Work out the wave speed.

Wave 1

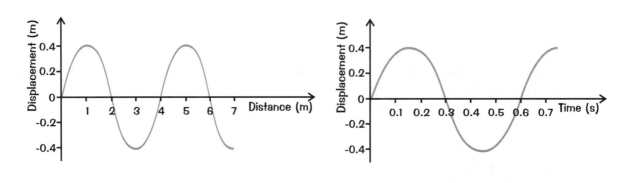

Wave 2

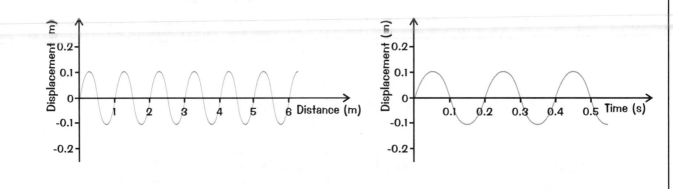

Nuclear Radiation

The Constituents of the Atom

The diagram below shows a lithium atom:

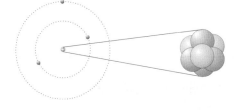

Where:

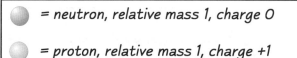

⬤	= neutron, relative mass 1, charge 0
⚪	= proton, relative mass 1, charge +1
·	= electron, relative mass 1/2000, charge –1

You write the symbol for this atom: $_{3}^{7}Li$

where 3 is the number of protons in the nucleus (the atomic number) and 7 is the total number of protons and neutrons in the nucleus (the mass number).

Three Kinds of Nuclear Radiation

There are three kinds of nuclear radiation you need to know about.

Alpha Radiation (Symbol α)

An alpha particle is emitted from the nucleus:

It is made up of two protons and two neutrons.

As a result, the atomic number of the original atom goes down by 2 and the mass number goes down by 4. E.g. the alpha decay of radium-226:

$$_{88}^{226}Ra \rightarrow {}_{86}^{222}Rn + {}_{2}^{4}\alpha$$

Beta Radiation (Symbol β)

A neutron in the nucleus turns into a proton and an electron — the electron is emitted from the nucleus and is called a beta particle. As a result the atomic number of the nucleus goes up by 1, but the mass number doesn't change. E.g. the beta decay of radium-228:

$$_{88}^{228}Ra \rightarrow {}_{89}^{228}Ac + {}_{-1}^{0}\beta$$

Nuclear Radiation

Gamma Radiation (Symbol γ)

High-energy electromagnetic radiation, known as gamma radiation, is emitted from the nucleus. The number of protons and neutrons in the nucleus stays the same.
E.g. the gamma decay of iodine-131:

$$^{131}_{53}I \rightarrow ^{131}_{53}I + ^{0}_{0}\gamma$$

N.B. When a nucleus emits any of these forms of radiation, it's called decay. By decaying, a nucleus reduces its energy, making it more stable.

Have a go at these questions:

1) State how many protons and how many neutrons there are in each of the following nuclei:

a) $^{241}_{95}Am$　　b) $^{239}_{94}Pu$　　c) $^{90}_{38}Sr$　　d) $^{60}_{27}Co$　　e) $^{226}_{88}Ra$

2) Copy and complete the following decay equations, making sure that you put the correct atomic and mass numbers for the nuclei:

$$^{242}_{94}Pu \rightarrow \underset{-}{-}U + ^{4}_{2}\alpha$$

$$\underset{-}{-}K \rightarrow ^{40}_{20}Ca + ^{0}_{-1}\beta$$

$$^{222}_{86}Rn \rightarrow ^{218}_{84}Po + \underset{-}{-}-$$

$$^{60}_{27}Co \rightarrow \underset{-}{-}\underline{\ \ } + ^{0}_{0}\gamma$$

$$^{14}_{6}C \rightarrow \underset{-}{-}N + ^{0}_{-1}\beta$$

Answers

1) (a) 95, 146
   (b) 94, 145
   (c) 38, 52
   (d) 27, 33
   (e) 88, 138

2) $^{242}_{94}Pu \rightarrow ^{238}_{92}U + ^{4}_{2}\alpha$

   $^{40}_{19}K \rightarrow ^{40}_{20}Ca + ^{0}_{-1}\beta$

   $^{222}_{86}Rn \rightarrow ^{218}_{84}Po + ^{4}_{2}\alpha$

   $^{60}_{27}Co \rightarrow ^{60}_{27}Co + ^{0}_{0}\gamma$

   $^{14}_{6}C \rightarrow ^{14}_{7}N + ^{0}_{-1}\beta$

Reliability and Validity

Evidence is Reliable If It Can be Repeated

Scientific evidence needs to be reliable (or reproducible). If it isn't, then it doesn't really help you.

When you're doing an investigation, you need to repeat your experiment several times to make sure your results are reliable — you should get round about the same answer each time.

> RELIABLE *means the results can be consistently reproduced in independent experiments.*

> *Example*
>
> *In 1989, two scientists claimed that they'd produced 'cold fusion' (the energy source from the Sun at room temperature). It was huge news — if true, it could have meant clean energy from sea water. But other scientists just couldn't get the same results — they weren't reliable. And until they are, the scientific community won't take cold fusion seriously.*

Evidence Also Needs to be Valid and Representative

Collecting reliable data is important, but if the data doesn't answer your original question, it won't be any use. You need to think about what data to collect to make sure your results will be valid.

> VALID *means that the data is reliable* AND *answers the original question.*

It's also important that you base your data on a big enough sample. The danger with a small sample is that your data might only be true for that sample — you won't be able to extend your results to other situations because they aren't representative of the whole population.

Controlling All the Variables is Really Hard

The difficulty with a lot of scientific investigations is that it's very hard to control all the variables that might (just might) be having an effect.

> *Example*
>
> *Studies have shown a correlation between the variables "presence of power lines" and "incidence of cancer". But this doesn't prove that power lines cause cancer — other explanations are possible. For example, power lines are often near busy roads, so it might be that living in an area of high pollution increases the incidence of cancer and that the power lines have no effect.*

In the lab it's different — scientists can control the variables so that the only one that changes is the one they're investigating — all the others are kept constant. In experiments like this, you can say that one variable causes the other one to change because you have made sure that nothing else could be causing the change.

You Don't Need to Lie to Make Things Biased

When you write up your results, it's important to give a balanced view of the data so that the reader can make up their own mind about it. People who want to make a point can sometimes present data in a biased way to suit their own purposes — e.g. by only using the bits of data that support their argument, or by phrasing things in a leading way.

Graphs and Relationships

Repeating an Experiment Lets You Find a Mean Result

If you repeat an experiment, your results will usually be slightly different each time you do it.
You can use the mean (or average) of the measurements to represent all the values.
The more times you repeat the experiment the more reliable the average will be.
To find the mean:

ADD TOGETHER all the data values then DIVIDE by the total number of values in the sample.

Graphs Are Used to Show Relationships

Once you've collected all your data and worked out the mean results, you need to analyse it to find any relationships between the variables. The easiest way to do this is to draw a graph, then describe what you see.

Example

Jamie did an experiment to see how the length of a wire changed depending on the weight hanging on it.
He gradually added loads up to 10 kg to the wire.
For each mass he measured the new length of the wire.

Jamie has drawn a scattergram to see if the two variables are related. He has included a line of best fit, which shows the correlation between load and extension.

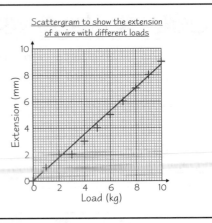

Scattergram to show the extension of a wire with different loads

Drawing Graphs is Easy — When You Know How

Scattergrams are really useful for showing whether variables are related, so make sure you know how to draw them.

1) Get your axes the right way round — the thing you change (the independent variable) goes on the x-axis. The thing you measure (the dependent variable) goes on the y-axis.

2) Think about the scale to use on each axis. You should make the most of the space you have by spreading the points out so that you can see what's going on.

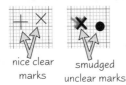

nice clear marks   smudged unclear marks

3) Plot the data points — use a sharp pencil and make a neat little cross.

4) Give your graph a title so it's clear what it's about.

5) Draw a line of best fit through your data. Try to draw the line through or as near to as many points as possible, ignoring anomalous results. Don't just connect up your data points — the line of best fit is meant to show the general trend in the data points, not their exact locations.

Correlation and Cause

Lines of Best Fit Are Used to Show Trends...

The line of best fit on Jamie's scattergram shows that as the load on the wire is <u>increased</u>, the extension of the wire also <u>increases</u>. This is called a <u>positive correlation</u>. The data points are all quite close to the line of best fit, so you can say the correlation is <u>strong</u>. If they were more spread out, the correlation would be <u>weak</u>.

Variables can also be <u>negatively correlated</u> — this means one variable <u>increases</u> as the other one <u>decreases</u>. Look at the way the line of best fit <u>slopes</u> to work out what sort of correlation your graph shows.

Sometimes the graph won't show any clear trend and you won't be able to draw a line of best fit. In this case, you say there's <u>no correlation</u> between the variables.

... and Estimate Values Between Data Points

When you do an experiment it's impossible to measure every data point. Instead, you can use the line of best fit to estimate values in between the data points that you actually measured — this is called <u>interpolation</u>. Or, you can use it to estimate values outside the range you measured — this is <u>extrapolation</u>. The method is the same for both — you draw a line from one axis to the line of best fit, then turn and go straight to the other axis and read off the value you end up at.

The estimates you get from <u>interpolation</u> are usually fairly <u>trustworthy</u> — if you've measured a series of points that show a clear trend, it's unlikely that anything weird will happen between them. <u>Extrapolation</u> can be a bit <u>dodgy</u> because it assumes your trend will continue in the same way. Take Jamie's graph — extrapolation predicts that a load of 100 kg would extend the wire by 84 mm. It might, but then again the wire might well snap long before this — you can't rely on the result.

Correlation Doesn't Always Mean Cause

Be careful what you conclude from an experiment — just because two variables are correlated, it doesn't necessarily mean that one causes the other.

In lab-based experiments like Jamie's, you can say that the independent variable causes the dependent variable to change — the extra load <u>causes</u> the wire to extend further. You can say this because everything else has stayed the same — nothing else could be causing the change.

Outside a lab, it can be much harder:

> ### Example
>
> Kate measures the speed of flow of a river and the diameter of the biggest rock that she can find at several points along its length, to see whether the two are related. Her results show a negative correlation between the variables — where the rocks on the river bed are biggest, the river flows more slowly.

From Kate's results, you can't say that bigger particles on the river bed cause the river to slow down. Neither can you say that a slower flow causes bigger particles to collect on the river bed. It could be either way round... or one change might not cause the other at all — you just can't tell.

Index